Y0-CAF-362

# The Philadelphia SPORTS WIZ Trivia QUIZ

by Jack Kreismer and Harry Patterson

Red-Letter Press, Inc.

THE PHILADELPHIA SPORTS WIZ TRIVIA QUIZ
Copyright ©2000 Red-Letter Press, Inc.
ISBN: 0-940462-92-3
All Rights Reserved
Printed in the United States of America

For information address:

Red-Letter Press, Inc.
P.O. Box 393, Saddle River, NJ 07458

# ACKNOWLEDGMENTS

Cover design
and typography: s.w.artz, inc.

Editorial: Ellen Fischbein

Contributors: Angela Demers
and Mike Ryan

## INTRODUCTION

Red-Letter Press proudly steps up to the plate with *The Philadelphia Sports Wiz Trivia Quiz*. Formatted in ten-question quizzes, it features an all-star selection of stumpers on the City of Brotherly Love's sports beat.

We bring you a book loaded with local trivia ... What Philadelphia-born baseball catcher won the National League MVP Award three times? ... In *Rocky III*, Rocky had a match with "Thunderlips" which was declared a draw after they threw each other out of the ring. Who played Thunderlips? ... Only once in baseball history did two brothers face each other as rookie starting pitchers. Do you know them?*

Now let's find out if you're a Philadelphia sports nut or not. Let the quizzes begin.

Jack Kreismer

Publisher

*The answers are: Roy Campanella ... Hulk Hogan ... Greg and Mike Maddux. (In 1986, the Cubs beat the Phils 8-3 with Greg on the mound for Chicago and Mike for Philadelphia.)

# IT'S AS EASY AS ABC

All of the answers to the following have either "A", "B" or "C" as the first letter of the last name.

1. Who was the last 76er to be named MVP of the NBA All-Star Game?

2. Do you know who sold the Eagles to Jeffrey Lurie in 1994?

3. Who am I? In 1959, I played 152 games at second base for the Phillies and never played another game in the big leagues. (Hint: My real first name is George.)

4. He's a three-time NHL MVP who led the Flyers to consecutive Stanley Cups in 1974 and 1975. Need we say more?

5. The Orlando Magic selected Chris Webber as the first overall pick in the 1993 NBA draft. Whom did the Sixers take with the second pick?

6. Whom did Jersey Joe Walcott defeat for the World Heavyweight Title in a bout held in Philadelphia on June 5, 1992?

7. Can you name the All-Pro defensive tackle who was tragically killed in a car accident in 1992?

8. Whom did Paul Owens replace as manager of the 1983 NL pennant-winning Phillies?

9. Three Phillies have been selected Rookie of the Year. Jack Sanford and Scott Rolen are two of them. Who's the third?

10. Who, in December, 1989 (three months after signing what was then the richest contract in NFL history) kicked a 91-yard punt – the third longest punt ever in pro ball?

# ANSWERS

1. Charles Barkley

2. Norman Braman

3. Sparky Anderson

4. Bobby Clarke

5. Shawn Bradley

6. Ezzard Charles

7. Jerome Brown (The Eagles kept Brown's locker intact throughout the season which was played in his memory.)

8. Pat Corrales

9. Dick Allen

10. Randall Cunningham

---

Sec. **82** Row **E** Seat **17**

Enter Gate B

"People say my ego is grand. I think it's in proportion to me."

*–NBA Hall of Famer Wilt Chamberlain*

# DEUCES

1. Name the only two NBA players to play more minutes than Wilt Chamberlain.

2. Which two ABA teams did Dr. J play for?

3. Name the two Sixers other than Wilt to win the NBA MVP.

4. Whom did the Sixers beat in the NBA Finals in their two championship seasons (1967 and 1983)?

5. Which two teams did the Flyers beat for their two Stanley Cups in the '70s?

6. Of the six 1967 NHL expansion teams the Flyers are one of four to remain in their original cities. Which two didn't?

7. Which two NFL teams did Chuck Fusina of the USFL Philadelphia Stars play for? (Hint: Two Bays, one before the Stars and one after)

8. Who were the Sixers two first-round picks in the 1980 NBA Draft?

9. Who were the Eagles two first-round picks in the 1973 NFL Draft?

10. The 1974 Vezina Trophy (best goalie) was shared by which Flyer and Chicago Blackhawk?

# ANSWERS

1. Kareem Abdul-Jabbar (57,546) and Elvin Hayes (50,000) — Wilt had 47,859.

2. The Virginia Squires and the New York Nets

3. Julius Erving (1981) and Moses Malone (1983)

4. The Warriors (1967) and the Lakers (1983)

5. The Bruins (1974) and the Sabres (1975)

6. The Oakland Seals and the Minnesota North Stars

7. Tampa Bay before and Green Bay after

8. Andrew Toney and Monti Davis

9. Charles Young and Jerry Sisemore

10. Bernie Parent and Tony Esposito

---

Sec. 07

Row 19

Seat 12

Enter
Gate C

Upper Tier

**"Any time you think you have the game conquered, the game will turn around and punch you in the face."**

*–Phillies Hall of Famer Mike Schmidt*

FULL SEASON TICKET

# THREES

1. Name the three cities Wilt Chamberlain played NBA basketball for.

2. Of the six 1967 NHL expansion teams, the Flyers are one of four to remain in their original cities. What are the other three?

3. In what three years did the Flyers make it to the Stanley Cup Finals during the '80s?

4. Who was the MVP for each of the three NBA All-Star Games held in Philadelphia (1960, 1970 and 1976)?

5. Whom did the Lakers get from the Sixers for Jerry Chambers, Archie Clark and Darrall Imhoff?

6. Steve Carlton was a Triple Crown pitcher for the Phillies in 1972, meaning he accomplished what?

7. The Phillies Chuck Klein was a Triple Crown hitter in 1933, meaning he accomplished what?

8. The Sixers had three first round draft picks in 1984. What three players did they choose?

9. In what three years were the Eagles NFL champs in the pre-Super Bowl days?

10. What did the Phillies' Mickey Morandini do in Pittsburgh on September 20, 1992 that had been done only eight times before in major league history?

# ANSWERS

1. Philadelphia, San Francisco and Los Angeles

2. Pittsburgh Penguins, LA Kings and St. Louis Blues

3. 1980, 1985, 1987

4. 1960 – Wilt Chamberlain (Warriors), 1970 – Willis Reed (Knicks), 1976 – Dave Bing (Washington Bullets)

5. Wilt Chamberlain

6. Led the league in wins, strike outs and earned run average

7. Led the league in home runs, batting average and RBIs

8. Charles Barkley, Leon Wood and Tom Sewell

9. 1948, 1949 and 1960

10. He fielded an unassisted triple play.

---

**FULL SEASON**

Sec. 17 Row K Seat 22 Gate F

"Man, that guy is ripped. I mean I've got the washboard stomach, too. It's just that mine has about two months of laundry on top of it."

*–Flyers left wing Shawn Burr, referring to the physique of Eric Lindros*

# FOUR-LETTER MEN

The solutions to the following clues are all four-letter last names.

1. He had the very first hit at the Vet on April 10, 1971.

2. Primarily a backup for the Eagles from 1961 to 1968, every so often this quarterback got to be king of the hill.

3. He was a four time All-America at La Salle and, as a rookie, was a member of the 1955 Warriors NBA championship team.

4. He took over the Eagles helm in 1999.

5. Formerly with the Cards and Braves, this outfielder closed out the 20th century with the Phillies.

6. He was the NFL's commissioner before Pete Rozelle.

7. It's the name of the stadium where Jim Bunning hurled his perfect game.

8. A baseball pioneer, he was known as the "tall tactician".

9. Like father, like son — This 1991 Eagles quarterback took after his dad who played that position for the Buffalo Bills. (Hint: His father also ran, unsuccessfully, for vice-president of the United States.

10. He played in a team record 163 games for the Phillies in 1979.

# ANSWERS

1. Larry Bowa
2. King Hill
3. Tom Gola
4. Andy Reid
5. Ron Gant
6. Bert Bell (who coached the Eagles from 1936 to 1940)
7. Shea
8. Connie Mack
9. Jeff Kemp
10. Pete Rose

"He's a lifeguard in the offseason. He can't swim, but he's great at wading."

*–Sixer GM Pat Williams, about 7' 6" Shawn Bradley*

**Sec. 16**

**Row 51**

**Seat 7a**

**Enter Gate G**
**Lower Tier**

# QUOTABLES

Below are ten quotes. Can you figure out who is quoted?

1. "You have to give Pete credit for what he's accomplished. He never went to college; the only book he ever read was *The Pete Rose Story*."

2. "Before the game they told me I looked like Babe Ruth. Then in my at-bat against Don Carman I looked like Dr. Ruth."

3. "Philadelphia is the only city where you can experience the thrill of victory and the agony of reading about it the next day."

4. "Errors are part of my image."

5. "Some of these people would boo a crack in the Liberty Bell."

6. "I tell myself that Jack Nicklaus probably has a lousy curve ball."

7. "Even Napoleon had his Watergate."

8. "Some days you tame the tiger. And some days the tiger has you for lunch."

9. "My family got all over me [for voting for George Bush] because they say Bush is only for rich people. Then I reminded them 'Hey, I'm rich.'"

10. "Take the shortest, quickest route to the puck and arrive in an ill humor."

# ANSWERS

1. Karolyn Rose (Pete's ex-wife)

2. John Kruk

3. Mike Schmidt

4. Dick Stuart

5. Pete Rose

6. Bob Walk (about his golf game)

7. Danny Ozark

8. Tug McGraw

9. Charles Barkley

10. Fred Shero

---

Sec. 07

Row 19

Seat 12

Enter
Gate C

Upper Tier

**"The scouts said I looked like Tarzan and played like Jane."**

*–Eagles defensive end Dennis Harrison, on why he wasn't drafted until the fourth round*

FULL SEASON TICKET

# HOME SWEET HOME

1. True or false? Baker Bowl, home to the Phillies from 1895 to 1938, was named after Home Run Baker.

2. Why did the Flyers play the last seven regular season home games in 1968 in New York City, Toronto and Quebec?

3. The Eagles have played home games in five different stadiums. How many can you name?

4. Both La Salle and Villanova play some of their home games at First Union Center. Do you know their other home venues?

5. In 1953, what was Shibe Park renamed?

6. Which college basketball team plays their home games at McGonigle Hall — Temple or Penn?

7. In what stadium was there a huge right field wall advertisement for a soap manufacturer which prompted fans to say, "The Phillies use Lifebuoy but they still stink"?

8. For experts only- He called himself Philadelphia's "Scientific Heckler" and was known as the "Iron Lung of Shibe Park" in the '50s. Was it  a) Pete Adelis  b) Pete Grey  c) Pete Runnels  or d) Pete Moss?

9. What stadium was home to the annual Army-Navy game before The Vet?

10. Who hit the first home run ever at Veterans Stadium? (Hint: If you know your Phillies players, we'll bet our "bottom dollar" you'll come up with it.)

# ANSWERS

1. False — It was named after William F. Baker, who owned the club from 1913 to 1930.

2. Because a part of the Spectrum roof had blown off (It was repaired in time for the playoffs.)

3. Baker Bowl, Municipal Stadium, Shibe Park, Franklin Field and The Vet

4. The Pavilion is also home to Villanova while La Salle plays some of their home games at Hayman Center.

5. Connie Mack Stadium

6. Temple — Penn plays at the Palestra.

7. Baker Bowl

8. A

9. John F. Kennedy Stadium

10. Don Money, in a 4-1 win over the Expos, April 10, 1971

---

**FULL SEASON**

Sec. 17
Row K
Seat 22
Gate F

**"He throws a "radio ball" — a pitch you hear but you don't see."**

*–Phillies manager Gene Mauch, about Sandy Koufax*

# YOUR NUMBER'S UP

Following is a list of athletes (and the team they played for) who've had their uniform numbers retired. How many can you name?

1. 15 (Eagles)
2. 10 (Sixers)
3. 1 (Flyers)
4. 20 (Phillies)
5. 99 (Eagles)
6. 7 (Flyers)
7. 36 (Phillies)
8. 40 (Eagles)
9. 24 (Sixers)
10. 60 (Eagles)

---

**"We never talked when I was in Chicago."**

*–Eagles coach Buddy Ryan, when asked if he and Bears coach Mike Ditka talked after Ryan left Chicago for Philadelphia*

| |
|---|
| **Sec. 16** |
| **Row 51** |
| **Seat 7a** |
| **Enter Gate G** Lower Tier |

# ANSWERS

1. Steve Van Buren
2. Maurice Cheeks
3. Bernie Parent
4. Mike Schmidt
5. Jerome Brown
6. Bill Barber
7. Robin Roberts
8. Tom Brookshier
9. Bobby Jones
10. Chuck Bednarik

| Sec. | Row | Seat |
|------|-----|------|
| 82 | E | 17 |

**Enter Gate B**

"Pete Rose is the most likable arrogant person I've ever met."

*−Phillies Hall of Famer Mike Schmidt*

# CLOSING IT OUT: HOOPS

What was the last NBA team each of the following played for?

1. Maurice Cheeks
2. Billy Cunningham
3. Darryl Dawkins
4. Manute Bol
5. Steve Mix
6. World B. Free
7. Lucious Jackson
8. George McGinnis
9. Clemon Johnson
10. Henry Bibby

---

Sec. 07

Row 19

Seat 12

Enter
Gate C
Upper Tier

"I never slept when I lost. I'd see the
sun come up without ever having
closed my eyes. I'd see those base hits
over and over and they'd drive me crazy."

*-Phillies Hall of Famer Robin Roberts*

FULL SEASON TICKET

# ANSWERS

1. NJ Nets ('93)
2. 76ers ('76)
3. Detroit Pistons ('89)
4. Golden State Warriors ('95)
5. LA Lakers ('83)
6. Houston Rockets ('88)
7. 76ers ('72)
8. Indiana Pacers ('82)
9. Seattle SuperSonics ('88)
10. San Diego Clippers ('81)

**FULL SEASON**

Sec. 17
Row K
Seat 22
Gate F

**"He signed me to a multi-day contract."**

*–Former Sixers GM Pat Williams, commenting on his status with owner Harold Katz*

# PASSING FADS

Listed below are the last names of Eagles passing-receiving combos. The letters are in their proper order, but the names have been combined. See if you can sort them out.
Example: VMACDNBORONCKALLIDN= Van Brocklin and McDonald

1. JREUTRGZELNASFEFN

2. HFORYYAINRG

3. SNJAECAKSODN

4. GACABRRMICIIIEALEL

5. JQAWUOIRSCKKI

6. CJAUNCNIKNSGHAOMN

7. MBACMRANHEOTNT

8. BBRAISVTAAROR

9. BYOORUYNLAG

10. LBIALSLMKANE

"Philadelphia fans boo funerals, an Easter egg hunt, a parade of armless vets and the Liberty Bell."

*–Phillies pitcher Bo Belinsky*

Sec. 16

Row 51

Seat 7a

**Enter Gate G**
Lower Tier

# ANSWERS

1. (Sonny) Jurgensen & (Pete) Retzlaff
2. (Bobby) Hoying & (Irving) Fryar
3. (Norm) Snead & (Harold) Jackson
4. (Roman) Gabriel & (Harold) Carmichael
5. (Ron) Jaworski & (Mike) Quick
6. (Randall) Cunningham & (Keith) Jackson
7. (Jim) McMahon & (Fred) Barnett
8. (Bubby) Bristar & (Mark) Bavaro
9. (Mike) Boryla & (Charles) Young
10. (Pete) Liske & (Gary) Ballman

| Sec. | Row | Seat | |
|------|-----|------|--|
| 82 | E | 17 | Enter Gate B |

"The world will end before there is another .400 hitter. I think that was mentioned in the Bible."

*–Phillies outfielder Lenny Dykstra*

# HOMETOWN HEROES

1. This Philadelphia-born athlete was an Olympic gold medal decathlon winner in 1968.

2. Born in nearby West Chester, PA this pitcher gave up Roberto Clemente's 3,000th and final hit of his career. (Hint: He played for the New York Mets.)

3. He was known as "The Reading Rifle."

4. He broke most of the southeastern Pennsylvania basketball scoring records while playing for Lower Merion High School.

5. He was born in Philadelphia and later went on to greatness as a cornerback for the Green Bay Packers. (Hint: He's first on the alphabetical list in the Pro Football Hall of Fame.)

6. At the time he retired, this player was the third highest scorer in NBA history, yet he never played high school basketball.

7. A Philly-born broadcaster, you might say this man opened up a whole wide world of sports for himself.

8. A Brooklyn Dodgers infielder, he was a Philadelphia "Brat."

9. This Philadelphian was a Temple basketball All-American guard in 1958 and went on to play for the Warriors in the NBA.

10. Out of Reading, PA this LPGA Hall of Famer won the 1989 and 1990 U.S. Women's Open and the 1992 LPGA Championship among other tournaments.

# ANSWERS

1. Bill Toomey

2. Jon Matlack

3. Carl Furillo

4. Kobe Bryant

5. Herb Adderley

6. Paul Arizin

7. Jim McKay

8. Eddie "The Brat" Stanky

9. Guy Rodgers

10. Betsy King

---

Sec. 07

Row 19

Seat 12

Enter
Gate C

Upper Tier

FULL SEASON TICKET

"I was told by a very smart man a long time ago that talent always beats experience. Because by the time you get experience, the talent's gone."

*–Phillies manager Pat Corrales*

# THE BIRDS
# AND THE BEES

Here we sting you with some fine-feathered zingers.

1. What 1926 NFL champs were named after a section of Philly?

2. This team picked up a number one NBA draft selection who formerly played with the Sixers.

3. An NCAA first team All-American in 1951, what was the nickname of Temple basketballer Bill Mlkvy?

4. True or false? Lady Bird Johnson once slam dunked at a 76ers game.

5. Who's the only pitcher in big league history to defeat the Boston Braves, Milwaukee Braves and Atlanta Braves?

6. In 1997, in their very first meeting ever, the Eagles tied this club, 10-10.

7. Garry Maddox connected for a game-deciding home run in the eighth inning of Game 1 of the World Series against what club?

8. Can you name the high-flying Eagle running back named to the NFL's 75th Anniversary All-Time Team?

9. They're the "other" Keystone State NHL team.

10. Who owned the Phillies before the current regime?

# ANSWERS

1. The Frankford Yellow Jackets

2. The Charlotte Hornets (The player was Derrick Coleman.)

3. "The Owl Without A Vowel"

4. False — but another First Lady did! At a 76ers-Pacers game in Indianapolis in 1988, Nancy Reagan appeared there to support the "clean team", an anti-drug program organized by the Pacers. Wayman Tisdale and Charles Barkley held her up for a promotional halftime dunk. She blew the first, but made the second.

5. Robin Roberts

6. The Baltimore Ravens

7. The Orioles

8. Steve Van Buren

9. The Penguins

10. Ruly Carpenter (The Carpenters sold the club after the 1981 season.)

---

**FULL SEASON**

Sec. 17
Row K
Seat 22
Gate F

**"I'd say I give it the old college try, except that I never went to college."**

*-The Sixers Darryl Dawkins, explaining his play in a particular game*

# ALL IN THE FAMILY

1. In a bout in Philadelphia in 1936 this fighter kayoed Phil Johnson in three rounds. Fourteen years later, the same boxer knocked out Harold Johnson, Phil's son, in three rounds in Philadelphia. Can you name this former heavyweight champ?

2. The Phillies were no-hit victims of what two brothers?

3. What baseball Hall of Famer tragically died when he choked on a piece of meat while dining with his brother?

4. He was the manager of the Philadelphia A's. His son played five games for the team over a three year span. Name them.

5. Two brothers both played on the Philadelphia Stars of the USFL. One was an offensive tackle and guard, the other a center who later played on two Super Bowl winners. Who are they?

6. In 1976, Mike Schmidt hit four homers in a game against the Cubs. Two were hit off what brotherly duo?

7. In 1948, the father played in a World Series with the Cleveland Indians. In 1980, his son played in a Series with the Phillies. Do you know them?

8. Two of his brothers played for the Raiders. He was a running back for the Eagles. Can you identify him?

9. What lefthanded-righthanded brother combination pitched in the same game for the Phillies against the Mets on June 12, 1964? (Hint: They "left their hearts in San Francisco" as the Mets drubbed them for an 11-3 loss.)

10. Sam "The Ram" rushed for more than 5,000 yards with the Patriots and his not so little brother later became a quarterback. Who is this brotherly tandem?

# ANSWERS

1. Jersey Joe Walcott

2. Bob and Ken Forsch. Bob no-hit the Phillies, 5-0, for the Cardinals in 1978 while Ken hurled a no-hitter for the Astros in 1979, over the Braves, 6-0. Bob also had one other no-hitter, against the Expos in 1983, 3-0.

3. Jimmie Foxx (at age 59)

4. Connie Mack and his son Earle

5. Brad and Bart Oates

6. Rick and Paul Reuschel (Schmidt's record-tying performance lifted the Phillies to an 18-16 win over Chicago at Wrigley Field.)

7. Ray and Bob Boone

8. Wilbert Montgomery

9. Dennis and Dave Bennett — Dennis started and lost the game while his brother worked the ninth inning.

10. Sam and Randall Cunningham

---

**"I'm 49 years old, and I'd like to live to be 50."**

*-Phillies manager Ed Sawyer, on why he quit piloting the woeful club*

**Sec. 16**

**Row 51**

**Seat 7a**

**Enter Gate G**
Lower Tier

# PHILLY POTPOURRI

1. Sixers guard World B. Free had his name legally changed to that. What was his original first name?

2. What was it that Phillies pitcher Ken Brett did on June 9, 13, 18 and 23 in 1975? (Hint: It wasn't on the mound.)

3. Who was the first NHL goalie to score a goal by shooting the puck into the other team's net?

4. What Phillies manager was the University of Delaware's second leading scorer and rebounder as a junior on the Blue Hens basketball team in 1954-'55?

5. Who holds the Eagles career rushing mark, Timmy Brown or Wilbert Montgomery?

6. Who coached the USFL's Philadelphia Stars to two championships?

7. What New York Met, after hitting his 100th career homer (off Phillies pitcher Dallas Green) on June 23, 1963, ran around the bases backwards in celebration?

8. What was notable about Jim Bivin pitching to Babe Ruth for the Phillies against the Braves at Baker Bowl on May 30, 1935?

9. Name the Dinka tribesman from the Sudan in Africa who played for the Sixers.

10. The Eagles set the record for the worst fourth quarter collapse in NFL history on December 1, 1985 when they held a 23-0 lead with 8:30 remaining and lost, 28-23. Who were their opponents?

# ANSWERS

1. Lloyd

2. He homered in four consecutive games.

3. The Flyers Ron Hextall, in a game against the Boston Bruins December 8, 1987

4. Dallas Green

5. Montgomery

6. Jim Mora

7. Jimmy Piersall

8. Bivin was the last man to pitch to Babe Ruth in a major league game.

9. Manute Bol

10. The Minnesota Vikings

---

Sec. **82**   Row **E**   Seat **17**

**Enter Gate B**

**"This isn't a body. It's a cruel family joke."**

*–Phillies pitcher Curt Schilling, poking fun at his own physical appearance*

# PUNCH LINES

1. Philadelphian Joe Frazier defeated Muhammad Ali in the "Fight of the Century" in 1971. The pair squared off in two more bouts. What were the outcomes?

2. The largest live attendance at a fight occurred at Philly's Sesqui-Centennial Stadium, September 23, 1926. "The Manassa Mauler" and " The Fighting Marine" wcre the combatants. What were their real names?

3. He played the role of a fighter in *Rocky V*, then played the role of a spoiler to delay George Foreman's comeback bid when he decisioned the former heavyweight champ. Who is he?

4. The last heavyweight title bout hcld in the city was at the Spectrum in 1968 when Oscar Bonavena unsuccessfully challenged what champ?

5. What son of a former heavyweight champ was a one-round knockout victim of Mike Tyson?

6. Walker Smith Jr. lost a 10-round middleweight decision to Joey Giardello in a 1963 Philadelphia fight. Do you know Smith's boxing name?

7. Born Maxwell Antonio Loach, he fought most of his bouts in Philly. What is his better known name? (Hint: He defeated Dwight Braxton for the light heavyweight crown.)

8. What former heavyweight champion, born Arnold Raymond Cream, fought most of his bouts in Philly and Camden?

9. Name the Philly-born trainer of Muhammad Ali.

10. James Francis Hagen, a light heavyweight champ from 1905 to 1912, went by what city-proud name?

# ANSWERS

1. Ali won both.

2. Jack Dempsey and Gene Tunney, respectively — Tunney took the heavyweight crown from Dempsey with a ten-round decision.

3. Tommy Morrison

4. Joe Frazier

5. Marvis Frazier

6. Sugar Ray Robinson

7. Matthew Saad Muhammad

8. Jersey Joe Walcott

9. Angelo Dundee

10. Philadelphia Jack O'Brien

---

Sec. 07

Row 19

Seat 12

Enter
Gate C
Upper Tier

**"That's right, Harry. I went to bed with a lot of old bats in my day."**

*–Baseballer turned broadcaster Richie Ashburn, explaining the good care he took of his baseball bats to his play-by-play partner, Harry Calas*

FULL SEASON TICKET

# THE HALL OF NAMES

Match the following nicknames and athletes.

1. "Chocolate Thunder"     a) Ron Jaworski
2. "Double X"              b) Darryl Dawkins
3. "Ol' Pete"             c) Lenny Dykstra
4. "Charlie Hustle"       d) Chuck Bednarik
5. "Jaws"                 e) Fred Carter
6. "Chink"                f) Ray Scott
7. "Concrete Charlie"     g) Steve Carlton
8. "Mad Dog"              h) Pete Rose
9. "Lefty"                i) Jimmie Foxx
10. "Nails"               j) Grover Cleveland Alexander

# ANSWERS

1. B
2. I
3. J
4. H
5. A
6. F
7. D
8. E
9. G
10. C

**FULL SEASON**

Sec.
17
Row
K
Seat
22
Gate
F

"If the fans want pretty skating, let 'em
go see an old Sonja Henie movie."

*–Flyers coach Fred Shero, defending
his Broad Street Bullies style of play*

# QUOTE, UNQUOTE

"I can't throw one, so…"
To complete the above quote by Phillies pitcher Curt Schilling on buying and naming his dog Slider, fill in the spaces based on the clues provided below and then insert the boxed letters in the corresponding blanks below.

1. Defensive lineman who penned *In the Trenches*
   _ _ _ _ (_) _  _ _ _ _ _

2. Phils lost to this team in '83 Series  (_) _ _ _ _ _ _ _ _

3. His HR gave NL All-Star win in '64
   _ _ _ _ _ _  _ _ _ _ _ _ (_) _

4. Self-deprecating catcher turned broadcaster
   _ _ _  (_) _ _ _ _ _

5. Sixers Allen Iverson went to college there
   _ _ _ _ (_) _ _ _ _ _

6. Led Flyers to two Stanley Cups  _ _ _ _  _ (_) _ _ _

7. Oakland QB who defeated Eagles in Super Bowl XV
   _ _ _  _ _ _ _ _ _(_)_

8. Turn of the century Phillies manager who took over in '97
   _ _ _ _ _  _ _ _ _ _ (_) _ _

9. Sixers traded Barkley to this team  _ _ _ _ (_) _ _

10. Eagles longtime play-by-play radio man
    _ _ _ _ _ _ _  _ _ (_) _ _

    _  _ _ _ _ _ _  _ _ _
    1   2 3 4 5 6 7   8 9 10

# ANSWERS

1. REGG(I)E WHITE
2. (B)ALTIMORE
3. JOHNNY CALLIS(O)N
4. BOB (U)ECKER
5. GEOR(G)ETOWN
6. FRED S(H)ERO
7. JIM PLUNKE(T)T
8. TERRY FRANC(O)NA
9. PHOE(N)IX
10. MERRILL RE(E)SE

Solution: "I bought one."

---

"You know what they do when the game is rained out? They go to the airport and boo bad landings."

*–Bob Uecker, about Phillies fans*

| Sec. 16 |
| Row 51 |
| Seat 7a |
| Enter Gate G Lower Tier |

# MULTIPLE CHOICE

1. He was the last NFLer to play without a face mask.
   a) Timmy Brown  b) Tommy McDonald  c) Ronald McDonald

2. Who shattered two backboards in a 22-day period in 1979, prompting the NBA to create collapsible rims?
   a) Darryl Dawkins  b) Moses Malone  c) Sam Malone

3. What former Bruins player netted the only goal in the Flyers 1-0 Stanley Cup win over Boston in 1974?
   a) Rick Macleish  b) Bill Barber  c) Red Barber

4. Pete Rose hit just one career grand slam homer, coincidentally off a pitcher who later became his manager. Who is he?
   a) Gene Mauch  b) Dallas Green  c) Mean Joe Greene

5. Whose rendition of *God Bless America* was a good luck charm for the Flyers?  a) Kate Smith  b) Peggy Lee  c) Spike Lee

6. What Phillie hit .196 in his first full year?
   a) Mike Schmidt  b) Dave Cash  c) Johnny Cash

7. Who was the first pro back to rush for 5,000 yards?
   a) Pete Pihos  b) Steve Van Buren  c) Martin Van Buren

8. Who scored the goal at the 1998 Winter Olympics to win the gold medal for the Czech Republic?
   a) Petr Svoboda  b) Michel Goulet  c) Robert Goulet

9. The 1966-67 NBA champion 76ers had a starting five of Wally Jones at the point, Hal Greer as the two guard, Wilt Chamberlain at center, Luke Jackson as the power forward and what player as the small forward?
   a) Neil Johnston  b) Chet Walker  c) Johnny Walker

10. Who was a member of the Phillies on the the 1983 and 1993 World Series teams?
    a) Larry Andersen  b) Charlie Hayes  c) Woody Hayes

# ANSWERS

1. B
2. A
3. A
4. B
5. A
6. A
7. B
8. A
9. B
10. A

| Sec. 07 | | |
| Row 19 | | FULL SEASON TICKET |
| Seat 12 | **"Nobody roots for Goliath."** | |
| | *–Wilt Chamberlain* | |
| Enter | | |
| Gate C | | |
| Upper Tier | | |

# STRAIGHT A'S

How well do you remember the Philadelphia Athletics?

1. The right field wall in Baker Bowl, where the A's home games were played, was what distance from home plate?
   a) 362 feet  b) 332 feet  c) 302 feet  d) 272 feet

2. Who, in 1951, became manager after Connie Mack?

3. What St. Louis Browns pitcher threw a no-hitter against the Athletics in his big league starting debut, May 6, 1953?

4. Who is credited with the introduction of dressing players in gray uniforms for road games?

5. Can you name the only player to hit 30 or more homers for twelve consecutive seasons?

6. What animal's emblem was worn on A's uniforms?

7. The 1929 and 1930 World Champion A's enabled the club to become the first team to win back-to-back Series twice. Do you know the pitcher who won the major league's e.r.a. title both of those years? (Hint: Think southpaw.)

8. The 1928 A's featured 41-year old left fielder Tris Speaker and 41-year old Ty Cobb in right, prompting the center fielder to say, "If this keeps up, by the end of the season, I'll be an old man myself." What Hall of Famer said that?

9. His real name is Cornelius McGillicuddy but you know him better as ____?

10. The 1927 A's had a record seven future Hall of Famers on their club: Ty Cobb, Eddie Collins, Zack Wheat, Jimmie Foxx, Lefty Grove, Al Simmons and their catcher. Can you identify him?

# ANSWERS

1. D

2. Jimmy Dykes

3. Bobo Holloman — He never pitched another complete game and was washed up by the end of the season.

4. Connie Mack

5. Jimmie Foxx

6. The elephant

7. Lefty Grove (In all, he won nine e.r.a. titles in his career.)

8. Al Simmons

9. Connie Mack

10. Mickey Cochrane

---

**FULL SEASON**

Sec. 17
Row K
Seat 22
Gate F

"**Losing streaks are funny. If you lose at the beginning, you got off to a bad start. If you lose in the middle of the season, you're in a slump. If you lose at the end, you're choking.**"

*–Phillies manager Gene Mauch, after his 1964 club blew a 6 1/2 game lead with only ten left to play and lost the NL pennant*

# THE ITALIAN STALLION, I-V

1. What real life fight was Sylvester Stallone's inspiration for the first *Rocky*?

2. In which Rocky did Rocky Balboa first become champ?

3. John Alvidson directed which two *Rockys*?

4. On what calendar date was Creed-Balboa I fought?

5. In which Rocky did Mickey (Burgess Meredith) die?

6. Carl Weathers (Apollo Creed) is a former pro athlete in which sport?

7. In addition to Stallone, Talia Shire (Adrian) and Burt Young (Paulie), Tony Burton was in all five Rockys. Whom did he play?

8. In which Rocky did Apollo die?

9. What was Mickey's last name?

10. What Philly disc jockey can be heard on the radio as Rocky chugs the raw eggs?

---

**"He can eat apples off a tree without using his hands."**

*–Eagles coach Norm Van Brocklin,*
*about 6'8" receiver Harold Carmichael*

**Sec. 16**

**Row 51**

**Seat 7a**

**Enter Gate G**
**Lower Tier**

# ANSWERS

1. Muhammad Ali vs. Chuck Wepner

2. *Rocky II*

3. The first and the last

4. July 4, 1976, the Bicentennial

5. *Rocky III*

6. Football — He was a backup linebacker for the Oakland Raiders.

7. He played Duke, Apollo's (and later Rocky's) trainer.

8. *Rocky IV*

9. Goldmill

10. Don Cannon

| Sec. | Row | Seat | |
|------|-----|------|---|
| 82 | E | 17 | Enter Gate B |

"The best thing about baseball is that you can do something about yesterday tomorrow."

–*Phillies second baseman Manny Trillo*

# THE PHILLIE FILES

1. Who's the only man to play on four different teams in the World Series?

2. This longtime Phillie shortstop holds the record for fewest home runs of any player with at least 7,500 at-bats. Who is he?

3. The Cy Young Award winner in the National League in 1980 also won two games in the World Series that year. Name him.

4. Who, in his last year in 1962 as a New York Met, hit .306?

5. Who won the N.L. Rookie of the Year Award in 1964 despite committing 41 errors?

6. What pitcher surrendered a career record of 502 home runs?

7. Who was the first hurler to win 100 games in each league in the 20th century?

8. What claim to fame does David Raymond hold?

9. The 1950 Whiz Kids clinched their pennant on the last day of the season when whose 10th inning homer beat the second place Dodgers?

10. He's the Vet home run king with 265 dingers, has more homers than any other player whose last name begins with the letter "S" (548), led the N.L. in homers eight times and won back-to-back MVP Awards in 1980 and 1981. His name is...?

# ANSWERS

1. Lonnie Smith (for the Phillies in 1980, Cardinals in 1982, Royals in 1985 and the Braves in 1991 and 1992)

2. Larry Bowa (15 homers in 8,418 at-bats)

3. Steve Carlton

4. Richie Ashburn (who had a .308 lifetime average and won the batting title twice during the '50s while with Philadelphia)

5. Richie Allen, whose .908 fielding average was the worst for a third baseman since 1914 (He did, however, hit .318 with 29 homers and 91 RBIs.)

6. Hall of Famer Robin Roberts

7. Jim Bunning

8. He was the first Phillie Phanatic.

9. Dick Sisler's

10. If you don't know the answer to this one, we're not tellin'!

---

**FULL SEASON**

Sec. 17
Row K
Seat 22
Gate F

> "Two-thirds of the earth is covered by water, the other one-third is covered by Garry Maddox."
>
> *–New York Mets announcer Ralph Kiner, about Philadelphia's slick-fielding center fielder*

# HOOP ALMA MATERS

Match each of the following with the school where he played college ball.

| | | |
|---|---|---|
| 1. Wilt Chamberlain | a) | Southwestern Louisiana |
| 2. Julius Erving | b) | None |
| 3. Maurice Cheeks | c) | Kansas |
| 4. Billy Cunningham | d) | Massachusetts |
| 5. Moses Malone | e) | West Texas State |
| 6. Hal Greer | f) | Duke |
| 7. Andrew Toney | g) | Auburn |
| 8. Charles Barkley | h) | Bridgeport |
| 9. Manute Bol | i) | North Carolina |
| 10. Johnny Dawkins | j) | Marshall |

**"I've got a great repertoire with my players."**

*–Phillies manager Danny Ozark*

Sec. 16

Row 51

Seat 7a

Enter
Gate G
Lower Tier

# ANSWERS

1. C
2. D
3. E
4. I
5. B
6. J
7. A
8. G
9. H
10. F

| Sec. | Row | Seat |
|------|-----|------|
| 82 | E | 17 |

Enter Gate B

"There's no one else in the league who's capable of scoring 50 goals and using you as a speed bump."

*–Shawn Antoski, on the Flyers Eric Lindros*

# REMEMBER THAT
# FABULOUS USFL

1. In what division did the USFL Philadelphia Stars compete?

2. Who was the owner of the team?

3. What USFL team did Reggie White play for?

4. The Stars ace running back Kelvin Bryant outran marquee player Herschel Walker for the 1984 season, but was still second to whom?

5. Which NFL team did the Stars David Trout previously kick for?

6. Name the Stars center who went on to a solid NFL career with the Giants and 49ers.

7. The Stars greatest game was their first playoff game in 1983 when they overcame a 38-17 deficit with 12 minutes to go to beat the Chicago Blitz. Who was Chicago's coach?

8. Whom did the Stars lose to in the first USFL Championship Game?

9. Whom did the Stars beat in the second USFL Championship Game?

10. What city did the Stars move to for their third and final season?

Bonus: The scheduled 1986 fall season never happened and Philadelphia was long gone, but the two four-team divisions were given distinctly Phillyesque names. What were they?

# ANSWERS

1. The Atlantic Division
2. Myles Tannenbaum
3. The Memphis Showboats
4. Joe Cribbs of the Birmingham Stallions
5. The Pittsburgh Steelers
6. Bart Oates
7. George Allen
8. The Michigan Panthers
9. The Arizona Wranglers
10. Baltimore

Bonus: The Liberty Division and the Independence Division

---

Sec. 07

Row 19

Seat 12

Enter
Gate C
Upper Tier

"I'm going to write a book — *How to Make a Small Fortune in Baseball.* You start with a large fortune."

*-Former Phillies owner Ruly Carpenter*

FULL SEASON TICKET

# PHILLY GOES HOLLYWOOD

1. Which Arnold Schwarzenegger movie co-starred Wilt Chamberlain as "Bombaata"?

2. What was the 1979 comedy in which Julius Erving was typecast as pro basketball player Moses Guthrie?

3. The 1996 Robert DeNiro thriller *The Fan* had a small role for which former Phillie?

4. Tom Hanks won an Oscar and Dr. J had a brief cameo as himself in what 1993 drama?

5. Name the real life former champ who appeared briefly as himself in the first *Rocky*.

6. How did Pete Rose's baseball ban affect his acting role as Ty Cobb in the TV movie *The Babe*?

7. Who played the character in 1989's *Major League* who had the same nickname as a certain Phillies reliever?

8. Which onetime Sixer had cameos as himself in *He Got Game*, *Space Jam*, *Forget Paris*, *Look Who's Talking Now* and *Hot Shots*?

9. Name the actor and actress who played Mr. and Mrs. Grover Cleveland Alexander in *The Winning Team*.

10. Which future Phillies manager had a small role as an anonymous ballplayer in that same 1952 flick?

# ANSWERS

1. *Conan the Destroyer*

2. *The Fish That Saved Pittsburgh*

3. John Kruk

4. *Philadelphia*

5. Joe Frazier

6. He was forbidden to wear any major league uniform.

7. Charlie Sheen played Ricky "Wild Thing" Vaughn. The Phillie reliever was Mitch "Wild Thing" Williams.

8. Charles Barkley

9. Ronald Reagan and Doris Day

10. Gene Mauch

---

**FULL SEASON**

Sec. 17
Row K
Seat 22
Gate F

**"I've discovered that the less I say, the more rumors I start."**

*–Flyers GM Bobby Clarke*

# WHO YOU TALKIN' 'BOUT?

Below are ten quotes and who spoke them. Can you figure out whom each was talking about?

1. "If you took those two legs and barbecued them, you'd have enough to feed a family for a month." -Larry Bowa

2. "He looks like a guy who went to fantasy camp and decided to stay." -Don Sutton

3. "He's so tall that if he fell down, he'd be halfway home." -Darryl Dawkins

4. "Sometimes I hit him like I used to hit Koufax, and that's like drinking coffee with a fork. Did you ever try that?" -Willie Stargell

5. "He must shower in Vaseline." -Lester Hayes

6. "[His] stare can put you on the disabled list." -Tim McCarver

7. "If I had as many singles as [him] I'd have worn a dress." -Mickey Mantle

8. "He has set the standards so high, his point totals are so enormous, that they've lost their impact." -Bill Russell

9. "He's so good on his jumper that it startles you when he misses." -Alex Hannum

10. "He's got a body like a Greek god and the running ability of a Greek goddess." -Dick Vitale

# ANSWERS

1. Greg Luzinski
2. John Kruk
3. Manute Bol
4. Steve Carlton
5. Randall Cunningham
6. Gene Mauch
7. Pete Rose
8. Wilt Chamberlain
9. Hal Greer
10. George McGinnis

---

"I wish they'd shut the gates, and let us play ball with no press and no fans."

*–Phillies first baseman Richie Allen*

| Sec. 16 |
| Row 51 |
| Seat 7a |
| Enter Gate G Lower Tier |

# THE HALL OF NAMES REVISITED

See if you can identify the name behind the nickname.

1. The Polish Rifle
2. Wild Thing
3. The Beast
4. The Fog
5. Dr. Strangeglove
6. The Vulture
7. The Secretary of Defense
8. The Baron
9. Pitchin' Paul
10. The Bull

# ANSWERS

1. Ron Jaworski
2. Mitch Williams
3. Clay Dalrymple
4. Jimmie Foxx
5. Dick Stuart
6. Phil Regan
7. Garry Maddox
8. Pete Retzlaff
9. Paul Arizin
10. Greg Luzinski

| Sec. | Row | Seat | Enter Gate B |
|------|-----|------|--------------|
| 82 | E | 17 | |

**"I went to see him about three times, and then he went to see a psychiatrist."**

*- The "Wild Thing", Phillies relief pitcher Mitch Williams, explaining his visits with a mental therapist*

# YOUR NUMBER'S UP - AGAIN

Identify the player by the retired uniform number.

1. 1 (Phillies)
2. 13 (Sixers)
3. 4 (Flyers)
4. 70 (Eagles)
5. 6 (Sixers)
6. 44 (Eagles)
7. 15 (Sixers)
8. 32 (Phillies)
9. 32 (Sixers)
10. 16 (Flyers)

# ANSWERS

1. Richie Ashburn
2. Wilt Chamberlain
3. Barry Ashbee
4. Al Wistert
5. Julius Erving
6. Pete Retzlaff
7. Hal Greer
8. Steve Carlton
9. Billy Cunningham
10. Bobby Clarke

**FULL SEASON**

Sec.
17
Row
K
Seat
22
Gate
F

**"The only way you can do that is by breaking into the equipment room."**

*–Pete Rose, retorting to Phillies outfielder Greg Luzinski's claim that he would steal 20 bases in a season*

# WHO AM I?

1. I was born in Philly and ruled the sport of pocket billiards when I won 15 world championships from 1941 to 1957.

2. I began my career with the St. Louis Cardinals but was traded to the Phillies. I struck out 4,136 batters, second only to Nolan Ryan.

3. I was shot by Ruth Steinhagen, a crazed fan, in 1949.

4. I was the number one NFL Draft pick in 1949.

5. I was born near Philadelphia in 1892 and am the only athlete elected to both the hockey and college football Halls of Fame. (Hint: Each year the best college hockey player receives a trophy in my name.)

6. I went to Overbrook High and hold a slew of NBA records— most games without fouling out in a career (1,218), most free throws missed in a game (22), most rebounds in a career (23,924), among them.

7. A native Philadelphian, I broke Bob Beamon's "unbeatable" long jump record in 1991 when I leaped 29' 4 1/2".

8. I came to Philly via Ohio State and was the 1980 World Series MVP.

9. I hailed from Philadelphia, won the U.S. National Tennis Championship (now the U.S. Open) six times during the '20s and was known as "Big Bill."

10. I coined the phrase "You Gotta Believe" when I was with the Mets and was a closer for the championship Phillies.

# ANSWERS

1. Willie Mosconi

2. Steve Carlton

3. Phillies first baseman Eddie Waitkus (He recovered to play the next year.)

4. Chuck Bednarik

5. Hobey Baker

6. Wilt Chamberlain

7. Mike Powell

8. Mike Schmidt

9. Bill Tilden

10. Tug McGraw

---

Sec. 07

Row 19

Seat 12

Enter
Gate C
Upper Tier

**"Statistics can be used to support anything, including statisticians."**

–Philadelphia Inquirer *writer Bill Lyon*

FULL SEASON TICKET

# BY ANY OTHER NAME

The answers to the following are not generally known by their given first names which are found in the following clues.

1. Charles played four seasons for the Sixers in the late '70s and his brother was a big league baseball pitcher during those years.

2. Robert is remembered more for his marriage to Mamie Van Doren than for his two mediocre seasons pitching for the Phillies.

3. Frank was an ace reliever for the Phillies in the '70s and '80s. His son became a country music star in the '90s.

4. George briefly rode the Steinbrenner Yankee manager merry-go-round after his stint as the Phillies skipper.

5. William, considered one of the founding fathers of baseball, managed the Phillies for 12 seasons in the 19th century.

6. Stanley managed the Phillies for a year during World War II and later managed the Yankees to a World Championship.

7. Cornelius stepped down as manager of the Philadelphia Athletics in 1950.

8. Lee led the NFL in receiving in 1973 for the Eagles with 67 receptions for 1,116 yards.

9. Glenn coached Temple's football team for six seasons in the '30s.

10. Christian tied an NFL record when he threw 32 TD passes in a single season for the Eagles.

# ANSWERS

1. Henry Bibby
2. Bo Belinsky
3. Tug McGraw
4. Dallas Green
5. Harry Wright
6. Bucky Harris
7. Connie Mack
8. Harold Carmichael
9. Pop Warner
10. Sonny Jurgensen

---

**FULL SEASON**

Sec. 17 Row K Seat 22 Gate F

"No matter what I talk about, I always get back to baseball."

*–Connie Mack*

# WHO 'DAT?

Identify each of the following.

1. During a 1999 game Phillies fans were warned of a possible forfeit to the Cardinals. Fifty years earlier the Phillies forfeited a game to the Giants after this player was ruled to have trapped a ball and the fans wouldn't stop littering the field.

2. He never won an NCAA Championship with St. Joseph's but his Trail Blazers defeated the Sixers in the Finals for an NBA Championship.

3. This once and future Flyer was the first NHL player to defect to the WHA and the first WHA player to defect back to the NHL.

4. He was NBA Rookie of the Year for the Warriors in 1958.

5. He was forced by Judge Landis to sell his interest in the Phillies after being accused of betting on his own team.

6. He is the only U.S. Senator who pitched a perfect game.

7. In 1985 he caught a 99-yard Ron Jaworski TD pass in overtime.

8. He has 240 regular season wins as well as 45 playoff wins as a Flyers goalie.

9. While pitching for the Athletics he gave up one of Babe Ruth's 60 homers in 1927. With the Red Sox in 1941 he gave up a hit to Joe DiMaggio during his 56-game streak.

10. He led the Eagles in rushing for four consecutive seasons (1987-'90).

# ANSWERS

1. Richie Ashburn
2. Jack Ramsey
3. Bernie Parent
4. Woody Sauldsberry
5. William D. Cox
6. Jim Bunning
7. Jim Quick
8. Ron Hextall
9. Lefty Grove
10. Randall Cunningham

---

| Sec. | Row | Seat | |
|------|-----|------|---|
| 82 | E | 17 | Enter Gate B |

"It doesn't take much to get me up for baseball. Once the National Anthem plays, I get chills; I even know the words to it now."

–Pete Rose, in 1981, his 19th year of big league baseball

# THE YEAR WAS ...

In what calendar year did each of the following take place?

1. The Phillie Phanatic makes his debut.

2. Mike Schmidt retires.

3. Wilt Chamberlain is traded to the Lakers.

4. The Philadelphia Athletics play their final game.

5. Ali-Frazier I

6. Ali-Frazier II

7. Ali-Frazier III (The Thrilla in Manila)

8. Longtime backup Sonny Jurgensen takes over for retired Norm Van Brocklin.

9. The Philadelphia Athletics lose to the Boston Braves in the World Series.

10. The Philadelphia Phillies lose to the Boston Red Sox in the World Series.

# ANSWERS

1. 1978
2. 1989
3. 1968
4. 1954
5. 1971
6. 1974
7. 1975
8. 1961
9. 1914
10. 1915

---

| Sec. 07 | "Let me get a good grip on that bat, as if | |
| Row 19 | I wanted to leave my fingerprints on the | |
| Seat 12 | wood; let me swing with a quick snap | FULL SEASON TICKET |
| | which comes from a powerful wrist, | |
| Enter | and, if I've gotten back of the ball, it | |
| Gate C | sure will travel." | |
| Upper Tier | *–Philadelphia A's Hall of Famer Jimmie Foxx* | |

# EAGLE I's

Following are clues to Philly footballers which all have the letter "i" in their names. We spotted you the i's. You do the rest.

1. A linebacker in 1983 and 1984, he went on to coach a pro team in another part of the state.  _ I _ _   _ _ _ _ _ _

2. He's the all-time team leader in pass receptions, yards and TDs.
_ _ _ _ _ _   _ _ _ _ I _ _ _ _ _

3. He quarterbacked the 1960 NFL Championship team.
_ _ _ _   _ _ _   _ _ _ _ _ I _ _

4. Though you might associate him more with another team, this Hall of Fame center played for the Eagles from 1964 to 1967.
_ I _   _ I _ _ _

5. He followed Dick Vermeil as head coach.
_ _ _ I _ _   _ _ _ _ _ _ _ _

6. A well-traveled running back, this player has had stints with the Dolphins, Patriots and Jets as well as the Eagles.
_ _ I _ _   _ _ _ _ _

7. He was a favorite target of Randall Cunningham.
_ I _ _   _ _ I _ _

8. He tied an Eagles single game record with four TDs in 1996.
I _ _ I _ _   _ _ _ _ _

9. He scored Philadelphia's first points in their only Super Bowl appearance, a 27-10 loss to the Raiders on January 25, 1981.
_ _ _ _   _ _ _ _ _ _ I _

10. This Eagles defensive end played Babe Ruth baseball on the same team as former Chicago Bulls star Michael Jordan.
_ _ _ _ _ _   _ I _ _ _ _ _

# ANSWERS

1. Bill Cowher
2. Harold Carmichael
3. Norm Van Brocklin
4. Jim Ringo
5. Marion Campbell
6. Keith Byars
7. Mike Quick
8. Irving Fryar
9. Tony Franklin
10. Clyde Simmons

FULL SEASON

Sec. 17
Row K
Seat 22
Gate F

"I never thought I'd lead the NBA in rebounding, but I got a lot of help from my teammates ... they did a lot missing."

–76ers center Moses Malone

# THERE'S A DRAFT
# IN HERE

1. Whom did Portland choose in the 1974 NBA Draft after winning a coin toss with the Sixers?

2. Whom did the Sixers then choose that year?

3. The previous season (1973) the Sixers won the toss and selected whom?

4. Who was the Sixers last #1 overall draft choice before Allen Iverson in 1996?

5. Who was the Flyers first pick in the 1967 NHL expansion draft?

6. Phillies draft choice JD Drew, who refused to sign with the team, was the Sporting News College Player of the Year for what year?

7. In what special NBA Draft category was Wilt Chamberlain chosen by the Warriors in 1959?

8. Which of the following was not a Sixers first round draft choice? Andrew Toney, Johnny Dawkins, Charles Smith or Al Henry?

9. The Eagles made halfback Jay Berwanger the very first NFL draft choice ever. What was the year?

10. What two-way future Hall of Famer did the Eagles pick as the first overall in the 1949 draft?

# ANSWERS

1. Bill Walton
2. Marvin Barnes
3. Doug Collins
4. Collins, in 1973
5. Bernie Parent
6. 1997
7. Territorial choice
8. Dawkins
9. 1935
10. Chuck Bednarik

"A good defense always beats a good offense, and vice versa."

*–Eagles coach Joe Kuharic*

| Sec. 16 |
|---------|
| **Row 51** |
| Seat 7a |
| **Enter Gate G** Lower Tier |

# PIGSKIN ALMA MATERS

Match each of the following pro footballers with the school where he played college ball.

1. Harold Carmichael
2. Sonny Jurgensen
3. Norm Van Brocklin
4. Steve Van Buren
5. Randall Cunningham
6. Ron Jaworski
7. Reggie White
8. Mike Quick
9. Donovan McNabb
10. Doug Pederson

a) Oregon
b) Youngstown State
c) Southern
d) Duke
e) Syracuse
f) Northeast Louisiana
g) North Carolina State
h) Tennessee
i) Nevada-Las Vegas
j) Louisiana State

**FULL SEASON**

Sec. 17 Row K Seat 22 Gate F

"I believe every person was put on Earth for a reason. Mine was to sell newspapers."

–*Eric Lindros of the Flyers*

# ANSWERS

1. C
2. D
3. A
4. J
5. I
6. B
7. H
8. G
9. E
10. F

---

Sec. 07

Row 19

Seat 12

Enter
Gate C
Upper Tier

"Football has affected my entire family's lifestyle. My little boy can't go to bed unless we give him a two-minute warning."

*–Eagles coach Dick Vermeil*

FULL SEASON TICKET

# ONE OR THE OTHER

1. Which pitcher started more games in his career — Steve Carlton or Nolan Ryan?

2. Which NHL team is older — the Flyers or the Islanders?

3. Of The Vet and St. Louis' Busch Stadium, which one has the larger capacity?

4. Who won the "Clash of the Legends" in Atlantic City in 1992 — Julius Erving or Kareem Abdul-Jabbar?

5. Who had the most triples in the majors in the 1970s — Larry Bowa or Rod Carew?

6. The Eagles played their first *Monday Night Football* game in 1970 against the Giants. Who won?

7. Saying that, "All he can do is catch touchdowns," which Eagles coach let wideout Cris Carter go — Buddy Ryan or Rich Kotite?

8. Which player entered baseball's Hall of Fame first — Mike Schmidt or Jim Bunning?

9. Who had the highest scoring average for a single season in the NBA — Wilt Chamberlain or Michael Jordan?

10. Which are there more of — Richie Ashburn home runs in the big leagues or Joe Frazier victories in the ring?

# ANSWERS

1. Nolan Ryan (773 to 709)

2. The Flyers — They began play in 1967 while the Islanders joined the league in 1972.

3. The Vet (62, 409 to 49,676)

4. The 44 year-old Abdul-Jabbar soundly defeated Erving, 42, by a 41-23 score.

5. Rod Carew, 80 (Bowa was second with 74.)

6. Philadelphia, 23-20

7. Buddy Ryan

8. Schmidt — He entered the Hall in 1995, Bunning in '96.

9. Wilt Chamberlain, 50.4 in 1961-'62

10. Joe Frazier had 34 wins in boxing while Richie Ashburn had 29 lifetime homers.

---

"Henry Aaron is the only ballplayer I have ever seen who goes to sleep at the plate. But trying to sneak a fastball past him is like trying to sneak the sunrise past a rooster."

*–Phillies pitcher Curt Simmons*

| |
|---|
| **Sec. 16** |
| **Row 51** |
| **Seat 7a** |
| **Enter Gate G** |
| Lower Tier |

# "THE" NICKNAMES

Name the sports figure known by each of the following nicknames.

1. "The Big Dipper"
2. "The Kangaroo Kid"
3. "The Prince of Mid-Air"
4. "The Fog"
5. "The Twirl"
6. "The Round Mound of Rebound"
7. "The Thief"
8. "The Hat"
9. "The Dutchman"
10. "The Minister of Defense"

| Sec. | Row | Seat | |
|------|-----|------|--|
| 82 | E | 17 | Enter Gate B |

"We lost every week. We lost to schools I never heard of. I think these guys used to get together and invent a school name just so they could play us. One year we lost to a school called 'We Want U.'"

*—Comedian Bill Cosby, remembering his futile football years at Temple University*

# ANSWERS

1. Wilt Chamberlain
2. Billy Cunningham
3. World B. Free
4. Fred Shero
5. Earl Cureton
6. Charles Barkley
7. Keith Allen
8. Harry Walker
9. Norm Van Brocklin
10. Reggie White

---

Sec. 07

Row 19

Seat 12

Enter
Gate C

Upper Tier

**"Like they say: It ain't over 'til the fat guy swings."**

*–Phillies catcher Darren Daulton, about the portulent John Kruk*

FULL SEASON TICKET

# WHO YOU TALKIN' 'BOUT? II

1. "Sometimes I look at him as my nephew, but sometimes only as my sister's son." -Gene Mauch

2. "I wish I had ten pitchers with his stuff and none with his head." -Gene Mauch

3. "Talking about [his] patience is like talking about Dolly Parton's elbows." -Sportswriter Marty Noble

4. "If there's a jerk connected with the Phillies, it's [him]. He's the All-American jerk." -Bucky Harris

5. "The Good Lord His Self couldn't manage [him]." -Phillies coach George Myatt

6. "When [he] is healthy, he's the finest player in the game. Some backs may run better, some might catch a pass better, some might do other things better. But overall, nobody's better." -Ron Jaworski

7. "[He] might have been the best pure passer of modern times." -George Allen

8. "You can talk about players who were bigger and faster, with harder shots. But show me a player who accomplished more." -Fred Shero

9. "Eighteen years ago I was a young businessman with a dream and [he] played a major part in making that dream come true." -Ed Snider

10. "I walked down there and asked him where he went to school. He said 'I go to Villanova.' I almost fell down. So I asked him if he'd like to come out for basketball, and he said 'Sure.'" -Al Severance

# ANSWERS

1. Roy Smalley
2. Bo Belinsky
3. Dallas Green
4. William D. Cox
5. Dick (then Richie) Allen
6. Wilbert Montgomery
7. Norm Van Brocklin
8. Bobby Clarke
9. Bernie Parent
10. Paul Arizin

FULL SEASON

Sec. 17
Row K
Seat 22
Gate F

"I've always said that today's newspaper is tomorrow's toilet paper."

*-76ers guard Allen Iverson, on the way the media portrays him*

# HARDBALL TRIVIA

1. What two teams participated in the first World Series played entirely on artificial turf?

2. With what team did Ty Cobb get his 4,000th hit?

3. Can you name the Cy Young Award winner with the fewest victories?

4. Do you know the Phillies/Red Sox slugger who hit more than 500 home runs and has a pitching percentage of 1.000?

5. Who wrote the book *Screwball*?

6. What former Phillie hit the first regular-season homer in the Astrodome? (Hint: He also played for the Cardinals, Dodgers, White Sox and A's.)

7. A first baseman on a pennant-winning team during the 1980s had 493 at bats without a single home run. Who is he?

8. Who surpassed Steve Carlton as the pitcher with the most Cy Young Awards?

9. Early Wynn is one of only two big leaguers to retire with exactly three hundred victories. Do you know the other one?

10. To what city did the Philadelphia A's move?

# ANSWERS

1. The Phillies and the Kansas City Royals, in 1980

2. The Philadelphia Athletics, in 1927 (ironically, against the Detroit Tigers)

3. Steve Bedrosian of the Phillies — He won five games.

4. Jimmie Foxx — He pitched one game for Boston in 1939 and nine games for the Phillies in 1945. His record was 1-0.

5. Tug McGraw

6. Dick Allen

7. Pete Rose, on the 1983 Phillies

8. Roger Clemens, with 5 (Both Carlton and Greg Maddux have 4.)

9. Lefty Grove, whose career mark was 300-141 in a 17-season career with the Philadelphia A's and Boston Red Sox

10. Kansas City (and then to Oakland)

---

**"Mike Anderson's limitations are limitless."**

> *-Phillies manager Danny Ozark, about his outfielder*

| Sec. 16 |
| --- |
| Row 51 |
| Seat 7a |
| Enter Gate G Lower Tier |

# BORN TO PLAY

Match each of the following with his birthplace.

1. John Kruk
2. Norm Van Brocklin
3. Joe Frazier
4. Randall Cunningham
5. Mike Schmidt
6. Julius Erving
7. Darren Daulton
8. Bobby Clarke
9. Bernie Parent
10. Charles Barkley

a) Dayton, Ohio
b) Eagle Butte, South Dakota
c) Leeds, Alabama
d) Montreal, Canada
e) Arkansas City, Kansas
f) Flin Flon, Manitoba, Canada
g) Roosevelt, NY
h) Santa Barbara, California
i) Beaufort, South Carolina
j) Charleston, West Virginia

| Sec. | Row | Seat | |
|------|-----|------|--|
| 82 | E | 17 | Enter Gate B |

**"When Steve and I die, we are going to be buried 60 feet, six inches apart."**

*–Phillies catcher Tim McCarver, about being Steve Carlton's "designated" backstop on the club*

# ANSWERS

1. J
2. B
3. I
4. H
5. A
6. G
7. E
8. F
9. D
10. C

Sec. 07

Row 19

Seat 12

Enter
Gate C

Upper Tier

**"I've been good for team unity, because everybody hates the same guy."**

*–Eagles coach Buddy Ryan*

FULL SEASON TICKET

# NOT QUITE SUPER EAGLES

The following all concern Super Bowl XV in 1981.

1. When the Eagles lost to the Raiders in Super Bowl XV what did each Eagle player get for the losers' share? Was it $54,000, $28,000, $14,500 or $9,000?

2. What future NFL head coach started at left tackle for the Raiders?

3. What was the game-day point spread?

4. Who caught Ron Jaworski's only TD pass that day?

5. Super Bowl MVP Jim Plunkett began the season on the bench. Who was the Raiders injured starting QB he took over for in week 5?

6. At what facility was the game played?

7. Name the kickers for each team.

8. Who set a Super Bowl record with an 80-yard TD catch?

9. Who was the Eagles cornerback he barely beat on that play?

10. Was it the Oakland or LA Raiders who faced the Eagles that day?

# ANSWERS

1. $9,000 — The Raiders got $18,000.

2. Art Shell

3. Eagles by 3

4. Tight end Keith Krepfle

5. Dan Pastorini

6. The Louisiana Superdome in New Orleans

7. Tony Franklin for the Eagles and Chris Bahr for the Raiders

8. Kenny King

9. Herman Edwards

10. Oakland — But you had to think for a second, didn't you?

FULL SEASON | Sec. 17 Row K Seat 22 Gate F

"He turned his life around. He used to be depressed and miserable. Now he's miserable and depressed."

*–Phillies play-by-play broadcaster Harry Calas, on outfielder Garry Maddox*

# TRUE OR FALSE?

1. The Flyers were the first of the modern NHL expansion teams to win a Stanley Cup.

2. The Mets and the Phillies were the only major league teams that Tug McGraw pitched for.

3. The Phillies have had the same nickname in the same city longer than any other pro sports franchise.

4. The official attendance of Wilt Chamberlain's 100 point scoring Warriors-Knicks game was less than 5000.

5. Joe Frazier boxed professionally in the '80s.

6. When the Raiders beat the Eagles in Super Bowl XV, they became the first wild card team to win a Super bowl.

7. The Eagles beat the Raiders in a regular season game that season.

8. Connie Mack was 87 years old when he managed his final game.

9. Bobby Clarke never won an NHL scoring title.

10. In 1943, during World War II, the Eagles and Steelers combined their teams and called themselves the Steagles.

# ANSWERS

1. True

2. True

3. True (since 1883)

4. True (4,124 to be exact)

5. True (in a 1981 draw with someone named Jumbo Cummings)

6. True

7. True (10-7 in week 12)

8. True — He died at age 93.

9. True — He finished second twice.

10. True

---

"The thing about him is that you know he is going to get to the basket; you just never know how."

*–The Sixers Bobby Jones, on teammate Julius Erving*

| | |
|---|---|
| **Sec. 16** | |
| **Row 51** | |
| **Seat 7a** | |
| **Enter Gate G** Lower Tier | |

# FLYER FLUMMOXERS

1. Who was the very first Flyer to win an individual NHL award?

2. Which NHL team originally drafted Eric Lindros in 1991?

3. Did Bobby Clarke average more or less than one point per game over his career?

4. What did Dave Schultz accumulate an astounding 472 of in the 1974-'75 season?

5. In the 1969-70 season the Flyers set an NHL record with 24 _____.

6. Who holds the Flyers team record for single season goals?

7. In the 1979-'80 season the Flyers set an NHL record by going 35 games without what?

8. The Flyers went to the Stanley Cup Finals three years in a row in the '70s, winning the first two. Whom did they lose to the third time?

9. What was Bernie Parent's first pro team?

10. Name the two Hockey Hall of Famers whose only NHL team was the Flyers.

# ANSWERS

1. Bobby Clarke won the Masterson Trophy for the 1971-'72 season.

2. Quebec Nordiques

3. More (1,058 over 1,144 games)

4. Penalty minutes

5. Ties

6. Reggie Leach (1975-'76)

7. Losing

8. Montreal

9. The Oklahoma City Blazers (Central Professional Hockey League)

10. Bobby Clarke and Bill Barber

# PRIZE PACKAGES

1. Who was the National League MVP in the Whiz Kids 1950 pennant-winning season?

2. Two Phillies hurlers were back to back Cy Young Award winners in 1982 and 1983. Can you name them?

3. The Flyers were Stanley Cup winners in 1974 and '75 but lost the title in 1976 to what team?

4. Who was coach of the 1985 NCAA basketball champion Villanova Wildcats?

5. In their only appearance in the Super Bowl, the Eagles lost to the Raiders, 27-10. What's the name of the trophy the Raiders won?

6. Who was selected as the number one pick in the 1991 NHL draft?

7. Name the only coach to defeat a Vince Lombardi- coached team in a a title game.

8. Who was chosen the World Series MVP when Baltimore defeated the Phillies in 1983?

9. What "fighter" was honored with a statue at the Spectrum?

10. Who has won more NBA MVP awards, Julius Erving or Moses Malone?

# ANSWERS

1. Jim Konstanty

2. Steve Carlton and John Denny

3. Montreal

4. Rollie Massimino

5. The Vince Lombardi Trophy

6. Eric Lindros (He was drafted by the Nordiques but sat out the 1991-92 season rather than play in Quebec. The Flyers acquired him in 1992 for six players, two number one picks and $15 million.)

7. Buck Shaw (in 1960, when the Eagles defeated the Packers for the NFL championship)

8. Rick Dempsey

9. Rocky Balboa

10. Malone — He was a three-time winner while Erving was an MVP just once.

---

**FULL SEASON**

Sec. 17
Row K
Seat 22
Gate F

"I've always prided myself on not striking out four times in a game. And I still haven't."

*-Phillies third baseman Scott Rolen, after striking out five times in a game against the Padres*

# PHILADELPHIA BEFUDDLERS

1. In the '40s the Phillies held a fan contest to rename the team. What was chosen?

2. Who spent his entire major league career as a Phillie before heading off to the Marlins and a World Series during the 1997 season?

3. Who was the Phillies' first black player? Was it Andrew Johnson, John Kennedy, Dick Nixon or Jimmy Carter?

4. Did Pete Rose hit more or less than 20% of his 4256 hits while wearing a Phillie uniform?

5. Future Pittsburgh Steeler coach Bill Cowher was a linebacker with the Eagles in 1983-84. Who was his head coach during those two seasons?

6. Who was the Flyers very first head coach?

7. What team became the 76ers following the 1962-'63 season?

8. When Wilt Chamberlain scored 100 points in 1962 he broke the record of 78 (which came in a triple overtime game). Whose record did he beat?

9. What ABA team did Wilt coach for a single season?

10. Can you name either of Philadelphia's Negro League baseball teams?

# ANSWERS

1. The Blue Jays (It was never official and was phased out by the end of the decade.)

2. Darren Daulton

3. John Kennedy

4. Less (826 or 19.4%)

5. Marion Campbell

6. Keith Allen

7. The Syracuse Nationals

8. His own, which came the previous season against the Lakers

9. The San Diego Conquistadors (1973-'74)

10. The Hillsdales and the Stars

---

| Sec. | Row | Seat | Enter Gate B |
|------|-----|------|--------------|
| 82 | E | 17 | |

"If you're associated with the Philadelphia media or town, you look for negatives ... I don't know if there's something in the air or something about their upbringing or they have too many hoagies, too much cream cheese."

*–Phillies Hall of Famer Mike Schmidt*

# SIXER STUMPERS

1. What did the Sixers "retire" in honor of announcer Dave Zinkoff?

2. For what ABA team did Billy Cunningham play for two seasons before returning to the Sixers?

3. Which Sixer won the very first NBA Sixth Man Award?

4. Who was the first Sixer to be named NBA Rookie of the Year?

5. Who was the first Sixer coach to be named NBA Coach of the Year?

6. Which team beat the Sixers 139-91 in Philadelphia in 1972?

7. Who was the first Penn State player drafted by the Sixers?

8. What tragic event caused a three day postponement of the Celtics-Sixers title series?

9. Which Hall of Famer played his entire 16 year career with the same team but only one season in Philadelphia?

10. Name the only member of the NBA 50th Anniversary Team who played the bulk of his career with the Philadelphia Warriors.

# ANSWERS

1. His microphone

2. The Carolina Cougars

3. Bobby Jones

4. Allen Iverson (1997)

5. Dolph Schayes (1966)

6. The Knicks

7. Dave Wohl (in 1971)

8. The assassination of Martin Luther King in 1968

9. Dolph Schayes (He retired a year after the Syracuse Nationals moved to Philadelphia.)

10. Paul Arizin

---

| Sec. 07 | | |
| --- | --- | --- |
| Row 19 | | |
| Seat 12 | | |
| Enter | | |
| Gate C | | |
| Upper Tier | | |

"**Ex-teams are like ex-wives. Deep, deep down, you know you can't stand them.**"

*–Ex-76er Charles Barkley*

FULL SEASON TICKET

# COLLEGE MONIKERS

What is the athletic team nickname for each of the following area schools?

1. Temple
2. Philadelphia University
3. Penn
4. Drexel
5. LaSalle
6. Cheyney
7. Villanova
8. University of the Sciences in Philadelphia (USP)
9. St. Joseph's
10. Philadelphia Community College

# ANSWERS

1. Owls
2. Rams
3. Quakers
4. Dragons
5. Explorers
6. Wolves
7. Wildcats
8. Blue Devils
9. Hawks
10. Colonials

# MORE QUOTABLES

Again, here are ten quotes. Can you tell who is quoted?
(Hint: One person is quoted twice and was already quoted
on the previous "Quotables" page. He is quoted a lot.)

1. "I was guarded so closely that I thought I was going to spend the rest of my life looking out at the world through wiggling fingers, forearms and elbows."

2. "How do you think being enshrined here [the NBA Hall of fame] with all these illustrious names feel to a guy who back in high school was only playing intramural ball?"

3. "I hate losing more than I like winning."

4. "I think I'm baseball's best ambassador. Nobody can sell the game the way I can."

5. "People think we make 3 million and 4 million a year. They don't realize that some of us only make 500 thousand."

6. "I am not a role model. Parents should be role models."

7. "I didn't tell any of the players they couldn't go downtown that week. And I didn't work them any harder than I did the rest of the year."

8. "I've become a better player by sitting on the bench."

9. "I held [Jim Taylor] down and watched the last five seconds run off the clock. I said 'You can get up now.... The game is over.'"

10. "If you keep the opposition on their behinds, they don't score goals."

# ANSWERS

1. Wilt Chamberlain
2. Paul Arizin
3. Charles Barkley
4. Pete Rose
5. Pete Incaviglia
6. Charles Barkley
7. Dick Vermeil
8. Randall Cunningham
9. Chuck Bednarik
10. Fred Shero

---

Sec. 07

Row 19

Seat 12

Enter
Gate C
Upper Tier

"**The cops picked me up on a street at
3 a.m. and fined me \$500 for being drunk
and \$100 for being with the Phillies.**"

*–Philadelphia catcher Bob Uecker*

FULL SEASON TICKET

# CLOSING IT OUT: PUCKS

What was the last NHL team each of the following played for before retiring?

1. Darryl Sittler
2. Allan Stanley
3. Dave Stanley
4. Rick MacLeish
5. Ross Lonsberry
6. Wayne Stevenson
7. Don Saleski
8. Gary Dornhoefer
9. Tom Bladon
10. Rich Sutter

| Sec. | Row | Seat | Enter Gate B |
|------|-----|------|--------------|
| 82 | E | 17 | |

"This is the only town where women wear insect repellent instead of perfume."

*-Phillies broadcaster Richie Ashburn, speaking about the Astros hometown, Houston*

# ANSWERS

1. Red Wings (1985)
2. Flyers (1969)
3. Sabres (1980)
4. Red Wings (1984)
5. Penguins (1981)
6. Capitols (1981)
7. Colorado Rockies (1980)
8. Flyers (1978)
9. Red Wings (1981)
10. Tampa Bay (1995)

Sec. 07

Row 19

Seat 12

Enter
Gate C
Upper Tier

**"There's no tougher way to make easy money than pro football."**

*–Eagles quarterback Norm Van Brocklin*

FULL SEASON TICKET

# CLOSING IT OUT: PIGSKIN

What was the last NFL team each of the following played for before retiring as a player?

1. Mike Quick
2. Ron Jaworski
3. John Cappelletti
4. Wilbert Montgomery
5. Tony Franklin
6. Guy Morriss
7. Tom Brookshier
8. Nate Ramsey
9. Jim Ringo
10. Harold Carmichael

---

**"I'm like a duck above water, but paddling like hell underneath."**

*– Flyers coach Fred Shero*

| Sec. 16 |
| Row 51 |
| Seat 7a |
| Enter Gate G |
| Lower Tier |

# ANSWERS

1. Eagles (1990)
2. Chiefs (1989)
3. Chargers (1983)
4. Lions (1985)
5. Dolphins (1988)
6. Patriots (1987)
7. Eagles (1961)
8. Saints (1973)
9. Eagles (1967)
10. Cowboys (1984)

Sec. 82 · Row E · Seat 17

Enter Gate B

**"The toughest thing about managing is standing up for nine innings."**

*–Philllies skipper Paul Owens*

# CLOSING IT OUT:
# HARDBALL

What was the final Major League Baseball team that each of the following played for before retiring as a player?

1. Richie Ashburn
2. Dick Allen
3. Grover Cleveland Alexander
4. Garry Maddox
5. Steve Carlton
6. Jimmie Foxx
7. Robin Roberts
8. Gene Mauch
9. Greg Luzinski
10. Bob Boone

# ANSWERS

1. Mets (1962)
2. A's (1977)
3. Phillies (1930)
4. Phillies (1986)
5. Twins (1988)
6. Phillies (1945)
7. Cubs (1966)
8. Red Sox (1957)
9. White Sox (1984)
10. Royals (1990)

"He's so thin the 76ers don't bother to take him on the road — they just fax him from town to town."

*-Woody Allen, about Philadephia center Manute Bol*

| Sec. 16 |
|---------|
| **Row 51** |
| Seat 7a |
| **Enter Gate G** Lower Tier |

# QUOTE, UNQUOTE II

"If horses won't eat it, I don't want …"

To complete the above quote about Astro Turf by former Phillies first baseman Richie Allen, fill in the spaces based on the clues provided below and then insert the boxed letters in the corresponding blanks below.

1. Pitcher who beat Braves in '61 to end Philly's 23 game losing streak _ _ _ _ _ _ _ _ _ _ (_)

2. Former Phillies home sometimes called "The Dump by the Hump" _ _ _ _ _ _ (_) _ _

3. First baseman traded by the Angels to Phils in '64 for a player to be named later, he became that player _ _ _ (_) _ _ _ _

4. '97 Senior Circuit Rookie of the Year _ _ _ _ _ _ (_) _ _

5. First sacker who began career with Tigers and Mets _ _ _ _ _ _ _ _ _ (_)

6. Whiz Kids were beaten by this club in 1950 Series (_) _ _ _ _ _ _

7. They edged Philly 15-14 in game four of '93 Series, the highest-scoring postseason game ever _ (_) _ _ _ _ _

8. Phillie with the most at-bats in a season, 701 in 1984 _ _ _ (_) _ _ _ _ _ _

9. He skippered Philly before Terry Francona _ (_) _ _ _ _ _ _ _

10. Philadelphia bested this team in the 1980 Series _ _ _ _ _ _ _ (_) _

_ _ _ _ _ _ _ _ _
1 2   3 4 5 6   7 8 9 10

# ANSWERS

1. JOHN BUZHARD(T)
2. BAKER B(O)WL
3. VIC (P)OWER
4. SCOTT RO(L)EN
5. RICO BROGN(A)
6. (Y)ANKEES
7. T(O)RONTO
8. JUA(N) SAMUEL
9. J(I)M FREGOSI
10. KANSAS CI(T)Y

Solution: "to play on it."

| Sec. | Row | Seat | |
|---|---|---|---|
| 82 | E | 17 | Enter Gate B |

"I told him who to watch. I said if you want to be a catcher, watch Johnny Bench. If you want to be a right-handed power hitter, watch Mike Schmidt. If you just want to be a hitter, watch me."

–Pete Rose, *explaining his instructions to his son, Pete Jr., on the art of hitting*